Gershwin

Wise Publications
London/New York/Paris/Sydney/
Copenhagen/Madrid

Exclusive Distributors:
Music Sales Limited
8/9 Frith Street, London W1V 5TZ, England.
Music Sales Pty Limited
120 Rothschild Avenue, Rosebery, NSW 2018, Australia.

Order No. AM952545
ISBN 0-7119-7128-5
This book © Copyright 1998
by Wise Publications

Compiled by Peter Evans
Music arranged by Stephen Duro
Music processed by Allegro Reproductions

Printed in the United Kingdom by
Halstan & Co Limited, Amersham, Buckinghamshire.

Your Guarantee of Quality
As publishers, we strive to produce every book to the highest commercial standards.

The music has been freshly engraved and the book has been carefully designed to minimise
awkward page turns and to make playing from it a real pleasure.

Particular care has been given to specifying acid-free, neutral-sized paper made from pulps
which have not been elemental chlorine bleached. This pulp is from farmed sustainable forests
and was produced with special regard for the environment.

Throughout, the printing and binding have been planned to ensure a sturdy, attractive publication
which should give years of enjoyment.

If your copy fails to meet our high standards, please inform us and we will gladly replace it.

Music Sales' complete catalogue describes thousands of titles and is available in full colour sections
by subject, direct from Music Sales Limited. Please state your areas of interest
and send a cheque/postal order for £1.50 for postage to:
Music Sales Limited, Newmarket Road, Bury St. Edmunds, Suffolk IP33 3YB.

Visit the Internet Music Shop at
http://www.musicsales.co.uk

A Foggy Day

Music & Lyrics by George Gershwin & Ira Gershwin

Moderately

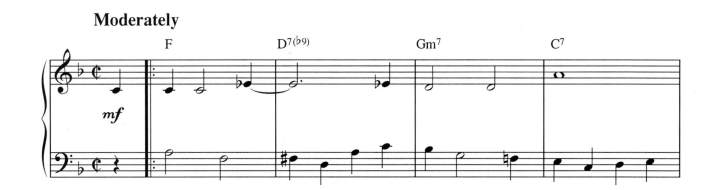

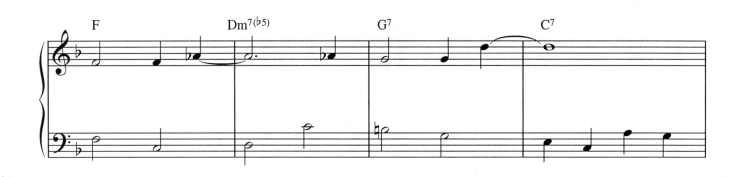

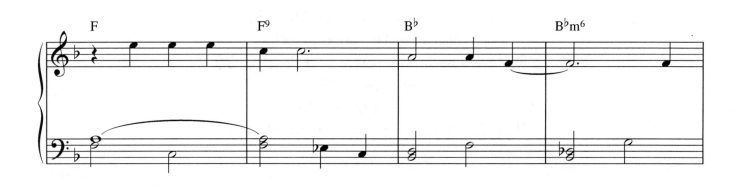

Bidin' My Time

Music & Lyrics by George Gershwin & Ira Gershwin

Moderately slow

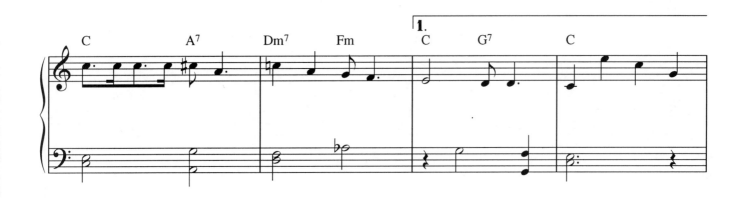

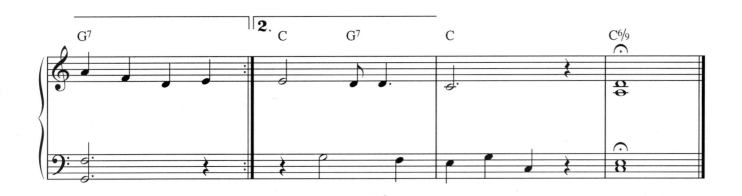

But Not For Me

Music & Lyrics by George Gershwin & Ira Gershwin

Moderately

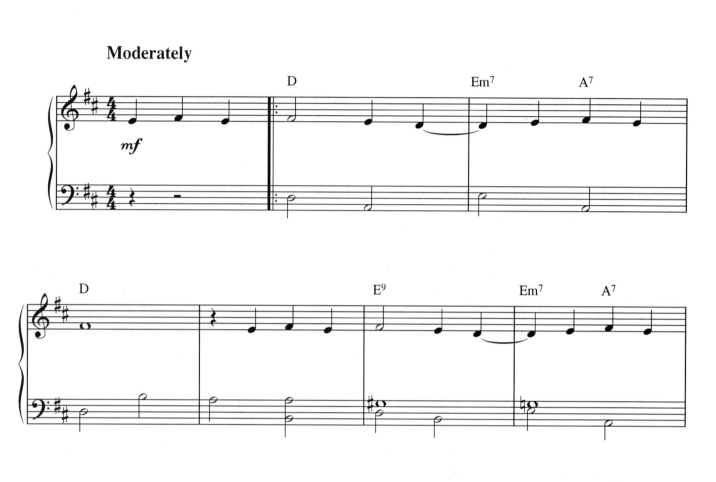

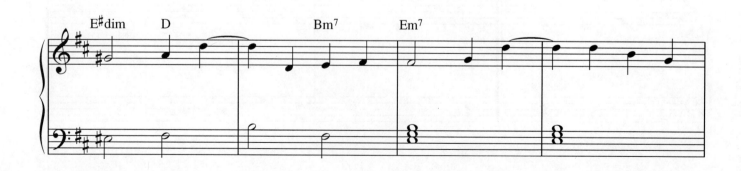

Embraceable You

Music & Lyrics by George Gershwin & Ira Gershwin

Moderately

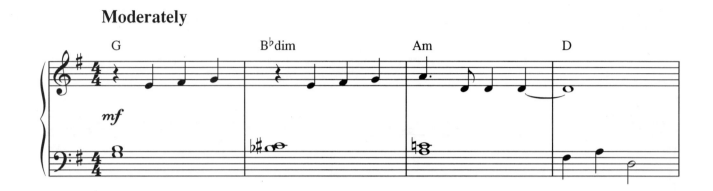

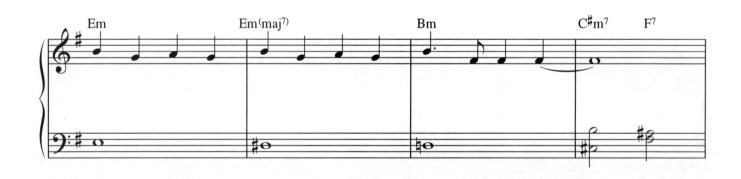

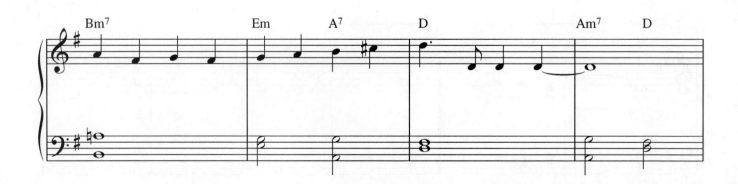

Fascinating Rhythm

Music & Lyrics by George Gershwin & Ira Gershwin

Moderately

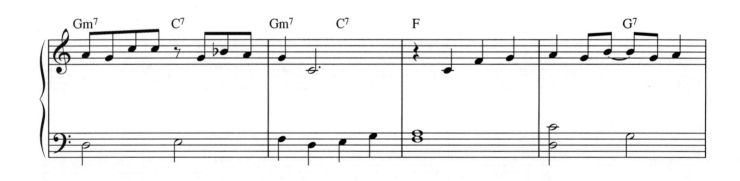

I Got Rhythm

Music & Lyrics by George Gershwin & Ira Gershwin

Moderately

Let's Call The Whole Thing Off

Music & Lyrics by George Gershwin & Ira Gershwin

Liza (All The Clouds'll Roll Away)

Music & Lyrics by George Gershwin, Ira Gershwin & Gus Kahn

Moderately

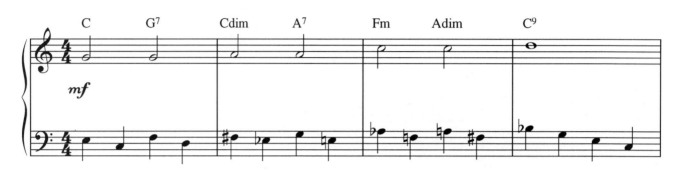

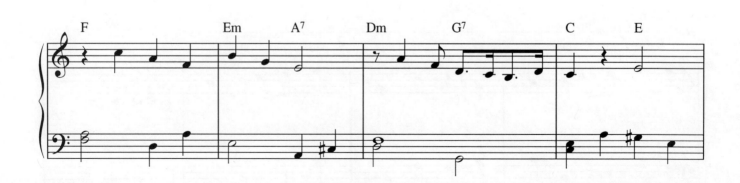

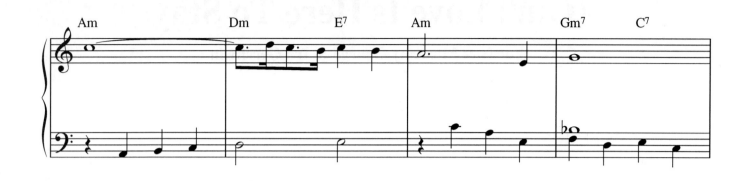

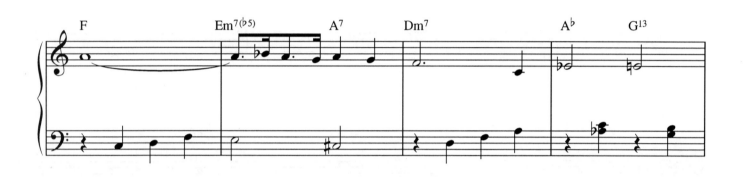

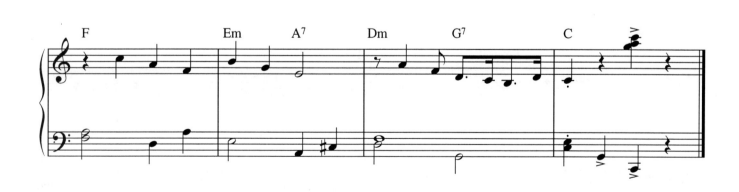

(Our) Love Is Here To Stay

Words & Music by George & Ira Gershwin

Moderately

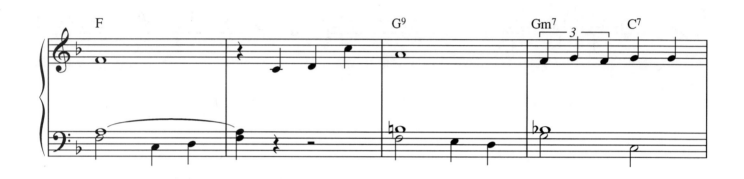

Love Walked In

Words & Music by George & Ira Gershwin

Nice Work If You Can Get It

Music & Lyrics by George Gershwin & Ira Gershwin

Moderately

Of Thee I Sing

Music & Lyrics by George Gershwin & Ira Gershwin

Moderately

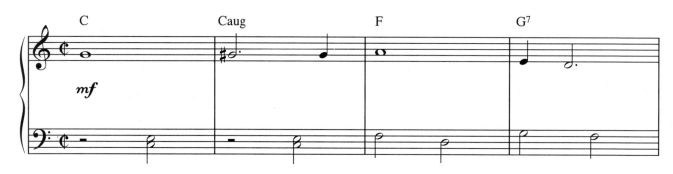

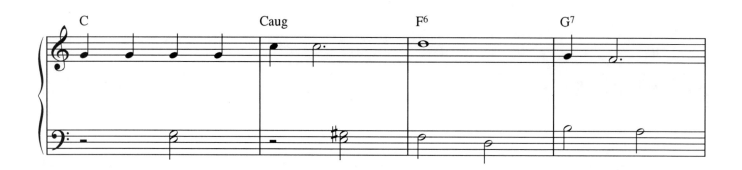

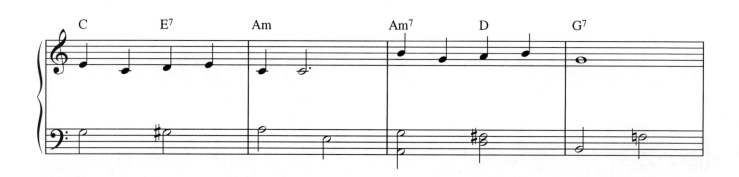

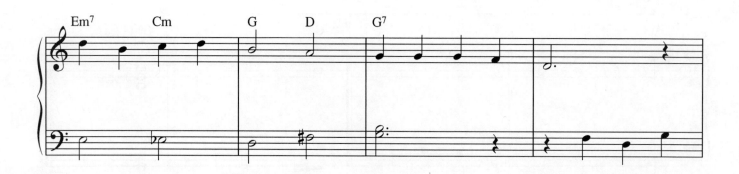

Oh, Lady, Be Good

Music & Lyrics by George Gershwin & Ira Gershwin

Somebody Loves Me

Music & Lyrics by George Gershwin, Ballard MacDonald &
B.G. DeSylva

Moderately

Someone To Watch Over Me

Music & Lyrics by George Gershwin & Ira Gershwin

Strike Up The Band

Music & Lyrics by George Gershwin & Ira Gershwin

Moderately

Summertime
(from "Porgy And Bess")

By George Gershwin, Ira Gershwin, DuBose & Dorothy Heyward

Swanee

Music & Lyrics by George Gershwin & Irving Caesar

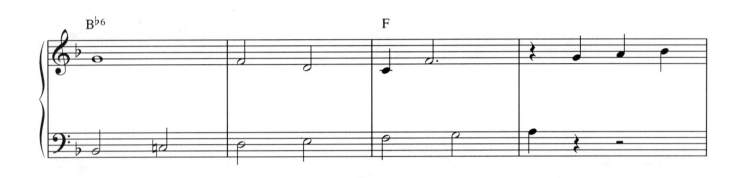

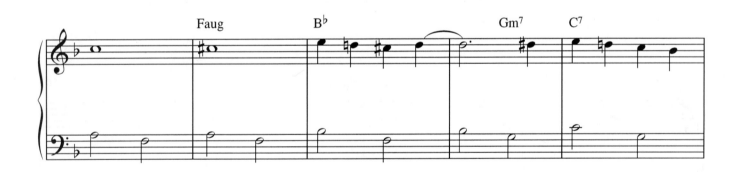

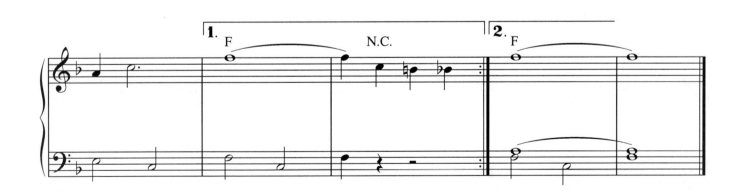

'S Wonderful

Music & Lyrics by George Gershwin & Ira Gershwin

Moderately

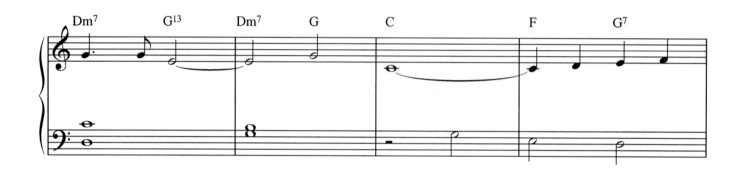

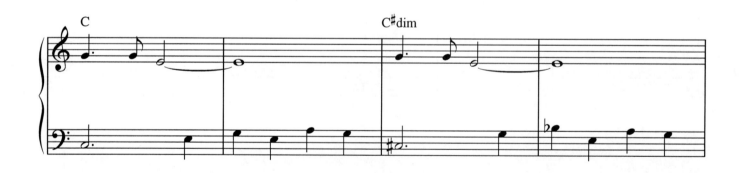

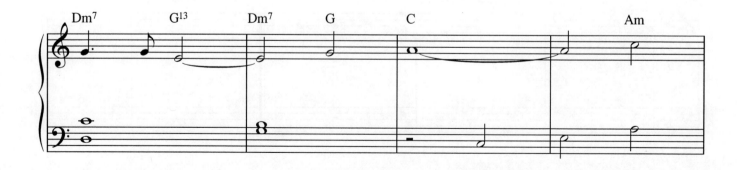

The Man I Love

Music & Lyrics by George Gershwin & Ira Gershwin

They Can't Take That Away From Me

Music & Lyrics by George Gershwin & Ira Gershwin

I Got Plenty Of Nuttin'

(from "Porgy And Bess")

Words & Music by George Gershwin, DuBose & Dorothy Heyward & Ira Gershwin

Moderately

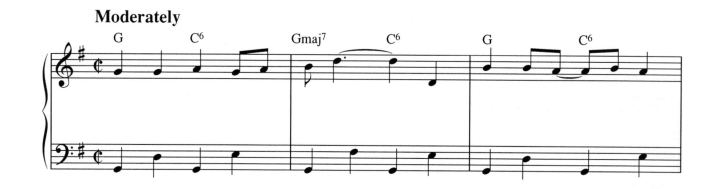

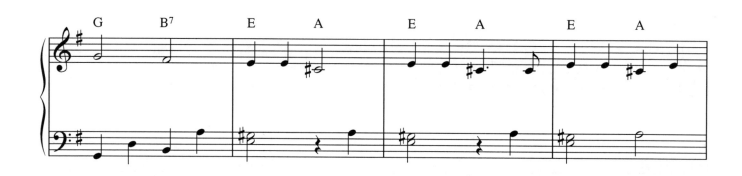

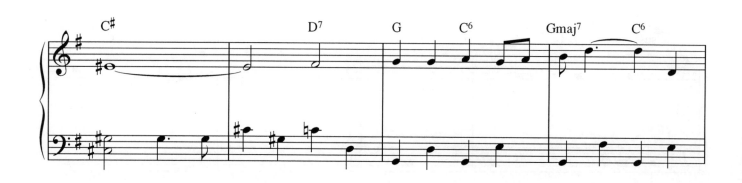

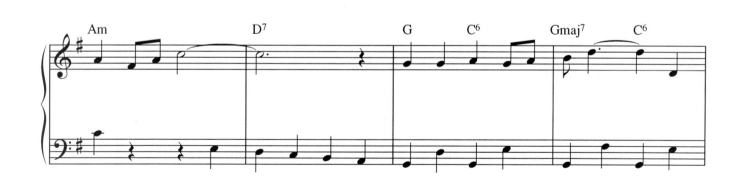

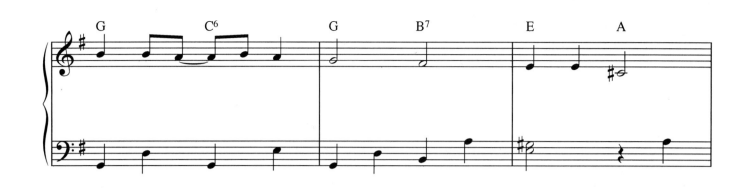

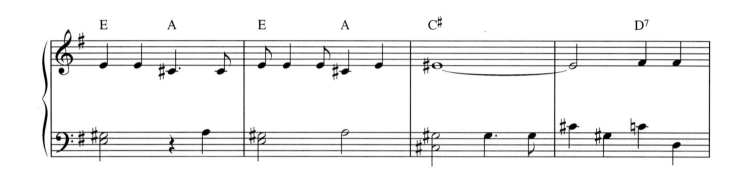

6/03 (47787)